ANIMALIA

Graeme Base

Within the pages of this book
You may discover, if you look
Beyond the spell of written words,
A hidden land of beasts and birds.

For many things are 'of a kind',
And those with keenest eyes will find
A thousand things, or maybe more—
It's up to you to keep the score.

A final word before we go;
There's one more thing you ought to know:
In Animalia, you see,
It's possible you might find *me*.
                    —Graeme

For Robyn

A Scholastic Book Club Edition

Harry N. Abrams, Inc., Publishers, New York

ISBN 0-590-44086-1   Copyright © Graeme Base, 1986   A Robert Sessions Book

An Armoured Armadillo Avoiding An Angry Alligator

FOUR
FAT
FROGS
FISHING
—FOR—
FRIGHTENED
FISH

GREAT GREEN GORILLAS GROWING GRAPES IN A GORGEOUS GLASS GREENHOUSE

Horrible hairy hogs

hurrying home-ward on heavily-harnessed horses

INGENIOUS
IGUANAS
IMPROVISING AN INTRICATE IMPROMPTU ON IMPOSSIBLY IMPRACTICAL INSTRUMENTS

· J O V I A L · J A C K A L S · J U G G L I N G · J U G S · O F · J E L L Y · I N · T H E · J U N G L E ·

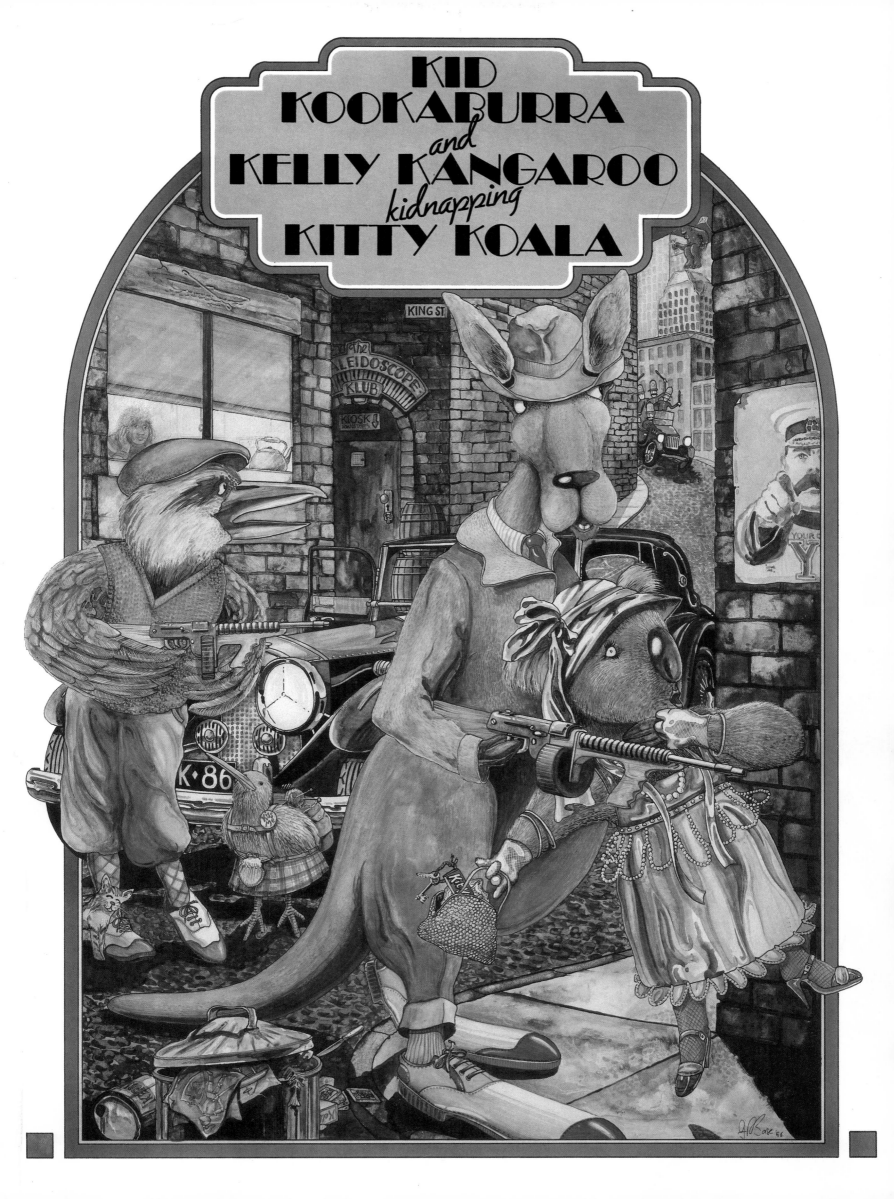

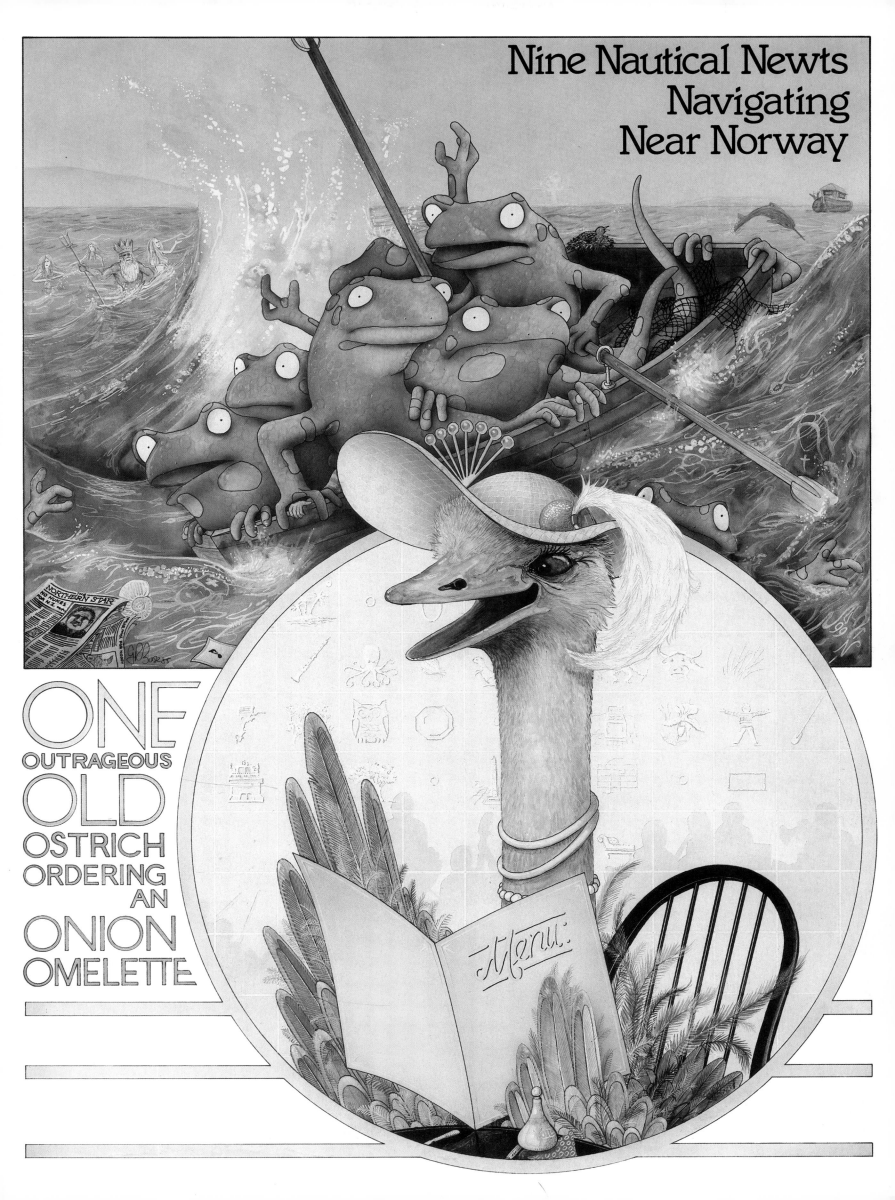

Proud Peacocks

Preening Perfect Plumage

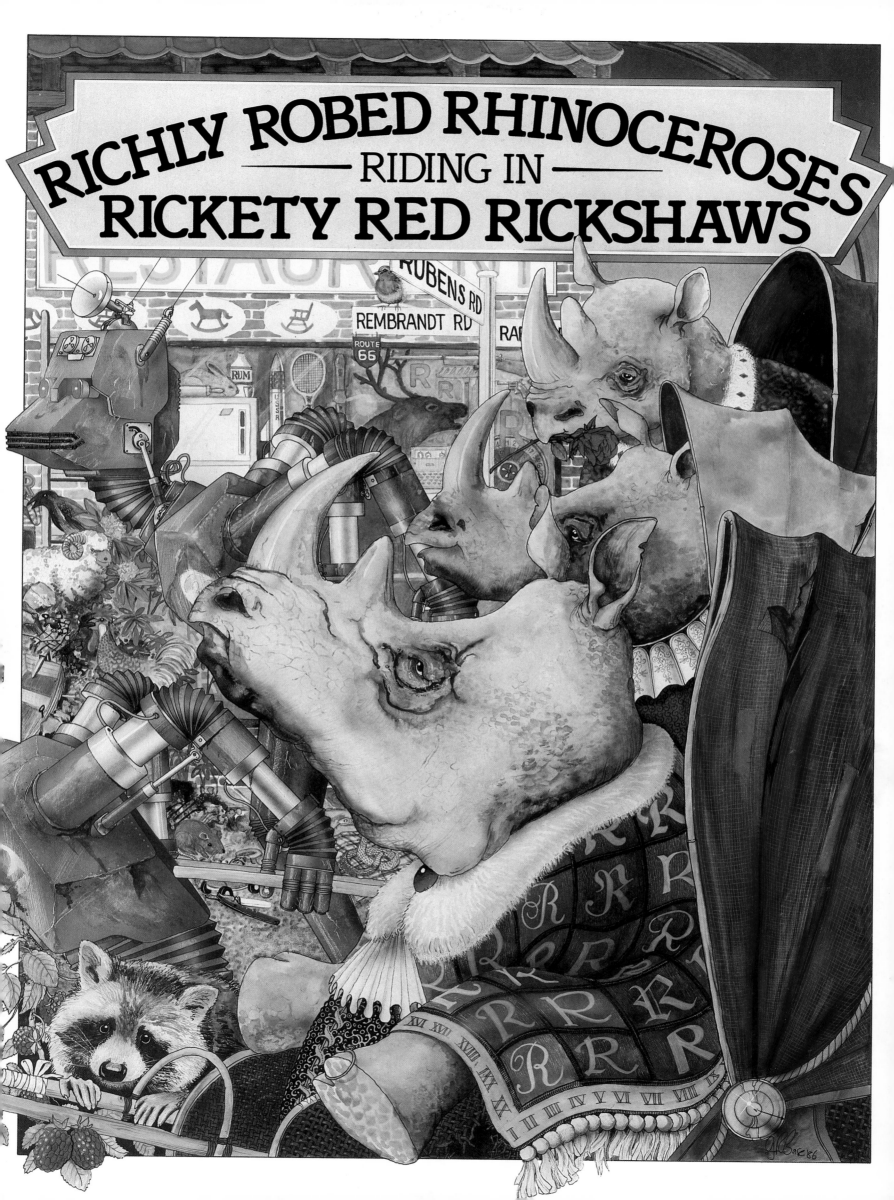

SIX · SLITHERING · SNAKES

SLIDING · SILENTLY · SOUTHWARD

SLIDING · SILENTLY · SOUTHWARD

SLIDING · SILENTLY · SOUTHWARD

SIX · SI

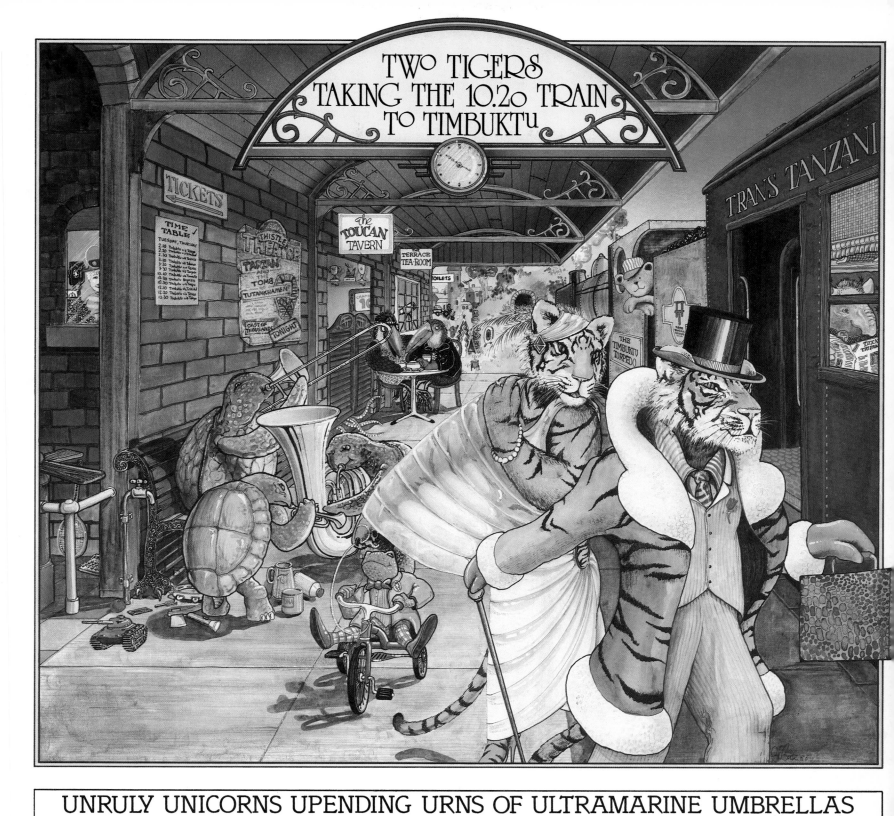

TWO TIGERS
TAKING THE 10.20 TRAIN
TO TIMBUKTU

UNRULY UNICORNS UPENDING URNS OF ULTRAMARINE UMBRELLAS

Wicked
Warrior
WASPS
wildly
waving
Warlike
Weapons

**YOUTHFUL YAKS YODELLING
IN YELLOW YACHTS**

Z. ZANY ZEBRAS ZIGZAGGING IN ZINC ZEPPELINS

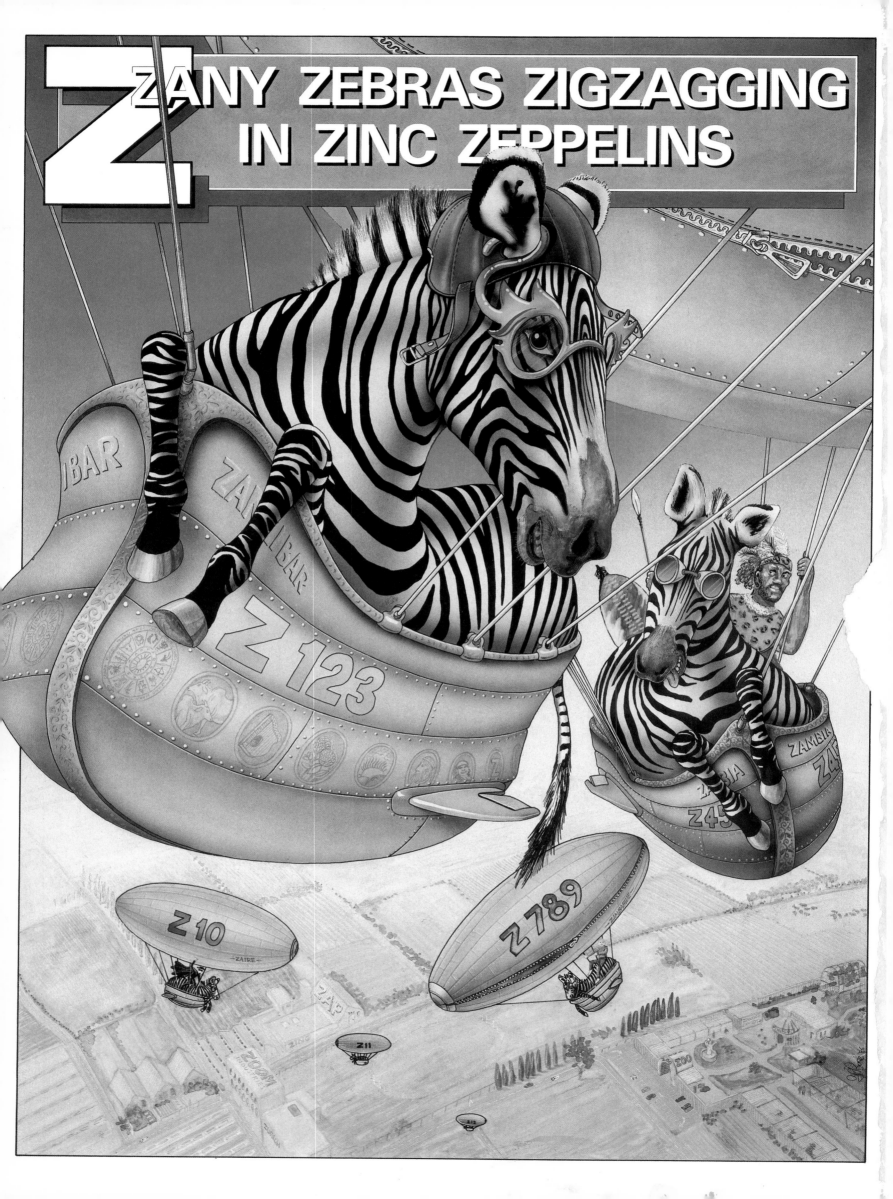